DADDLES

Boston · *LITTLE, BROWN AND COMPANY* · *Toronto*

DADDLES

The Story of a Plain Hound-dog

by RUTH SAWYER

Illustrated by Robert Frankenberg

LIBRARY OF CONGRESS CATALOG CARD NO. 64-10180

Fourth Printing

Published simultaneously in Canada
by Little, Brown & Company (Canada) Limited

PRINTED IN THE UNITED STATES OF AMERICA

DADDLES

PETERKIN and I loved Daddles — just terribly. We thought those two summers he belonged to us the very best we ever had. Peterkin was eleven that first summer and I was eight; and it all began with egg-trouble.

It is a funny thing about families and dogs — either they belong to each other or they don't. If you asked Peterkin and me — and Daddles — we would all have said we belonged to each other. But if you asked the Monroes — the meanest, dirtiest and most shiftless family in Haddock Harbor — they would have said he was their hound-dog.

If dogs belong to the whole family they usually belong to the grownups. That was the way in our family. We always had a dog — there was Lad, a collie, and

McJimsey, an Irish setter, and Rover, a Saint Bernard. There were others; and all of them belonged to our parents or our older brothers. Peterkin and I tried our best to claim them as ours. We threw sticks or old tennis balls for them to retrieve. We tried coaxing them along when we went on errands for Mother or when we went adventuring. We even tried to smuggle them into our rooms at night. But they would have none of us. We just didn't mean turnips to them.

Peterkin and I wanted dreadfully to have a dog of our own. We always had luck with strays — all mongrels, without collars and often with ragged bits of rope around their necks. They would follow us home. With Jo's help we would feed them a good dinner. We would scratch them, hug them, throw balls for them. But Mother would never let them stay more than one night. After a good breakfast we had to chase them up the lane and not let them come back. They never did.

The summer before I was eight we found a perfectly elegant stray. He began by being Airedale and ended by being spaniel. We just took to each other. But that night a skunk came along to forage in our garbage can. By that time, having had a good dinner and lots of romping together, the dog thought he belonged to us. So, of course, he protected us. He lit right into that skunk. Peterkin and I joined in; and it ended with a free-for-all. The skunk got off safely, but we got what the skunk left.

Our parents burned our clothes; and we were soaked in hot water and turpentine and scrubbed — scalp to toes. Even then we went about smelling something awful. We couldn't eat with the family or in the kitchen, so we took our plates out to the veranda. Mother said if we brought back another stray that summer we would lose our allowances and live on bread and water. Of course she didn't mean that — the bread and water. But in those years children were supposed to mind their parents; and when Mother laid down the law we were supposed to keep it. So that summer we had no more strays; and Peterkin and I were terribly lonesome for a dog of our own.

The following summer we counted on Mother having forgotten about the skunk; and Peterkin and I began with high hopes. We always came down to Maine on one of the old Boston and Bangor boats; and Ellis Freeman, the stage driver, always met us. Driving us up to the cottage he told us the news of Haddock Harbor, everything that had happened since we had left the fall before. This time he began, "Liza Bean's had her fifth baby. Old Cap'n Coombs died — coldest spell we had. Gramma Snow took first prize ag'in for her pies." And finally, "Hens hain't layin'. Nobody's got any eggs at the Harbor."

"What will we do?" Mother asked.

"Do without, same as the rest of us. Salt mackerel and smoked cod doan't make a bad meal if you know how to cook 'em." Then he offered a little bit of hope: "Seeing as folks at the Harbor set great store by you Wymans mebbe they'll spare you a few. No harm askin'."

That began our egg-trouble. Eggs in driblets, Mother said. One day at breakfast she got spunky. "We've got to have more eggs. You children take a basket and go up to the Monroes. They keep hens. See what you can get there." So that's how it happened that Peterkin and I walked the mile to the Monroe farm that day in early June. It was sunny and the air was full of good smells: apple blossoms, salt flats and pine needles. We liked the walk, but we didn't like the Monroes.

They were the dirtiest family, and their house smelled of the pigsty under their barn. There were three Monroes — Bill, Mat, and the woman who was wife to one of them. All the way there Peterkin and I argued over which one should ask for the eggs. "You should — you're older," I said.

But he said, "You should, Snoodie. You can be real coaxing when you try."

I might as well explain here that Peterkin and Snoodie were not our real names. In the winter our father read aloud to us, and out of the books he liked best he had picked our nicknames. They lasted until Peterkin went to prep school.

As we came near the Monroe farm we saw a hound-dog sitting on the kitchen stoop. Peterkin and I looked at each other. "You see what I see?" asked Peterkin.

"I see," said I. "And so far Mother has said nothing about stray dogs and losing our allowances this summer." With this happy thought we went the rest of the way a lot faster.

We threw down the basket, mounted the steps, and for at least ten minutes the eggs were forgotten. We sat down, one on each side of the hound-dog. I guess you would have called him a beagle. His legs were short, the front ones crooked. He was white with black and tan spots, long silky ears and the saddest eyes we had ever looked into. We hugged, scratched and patted him in turns. We could see he was as pleased to find us as we were to find him. He licked our hands and made little whimpering sounds. We were so full of dog-pleasure we never heard Bill Monroe come to the screen door. Not until he spoke: "What you-uns want?" His voice had a surly sound and I didn't like it. The hound-dog scrooched down between us and tried to make himself look like nothing at all.

Peterkin got to his feet and used his best manner. "Good morning, Mr. Monroe. Our mother would like to know if you could spare us a few eggs."

If we had asked for the Crown Jewels we couldn't have amazed him more. He looked at us, each in turn, and harrumped and finally asked, "You the Wyman young-uns?"

We agreed we were. He went inside and we heard him calling someone named "You, there!" There followed a lot of whispering. Then the Monroe wife came to the door, scowling. "What you-uns want?"

This time I answered, and if I had been a hot griddle butter wouldn't have melted faster. "Mrs. Monroe — all us Wymans would be much obliged if you could spare us a few eggs." She disappeared and there was another conference behind the screen door. All the time we and the hound-dog were belonging to each other faster and closer. The two finally came back together. "Cal'ate we can spare you six. Got a basket?"

That was the woman; but Bill Monroe said, " 'Twill cost you two bits."

Peterkin and I knew that was an awful amount to ask for six eggs. But we also knew enough not to haggle. So Peterkin handed in the basket and gave Bill Monroe the money. While we waited for the eggs Peterkin asked, trying to sound casual, "This your hound-dog? What's his name?"

Bill Monroe looked at us and the dog as mean as a man can look. "He's ourn all right. Bein' a plain hound-dog he hain't got a name."

We left — hoping the hound-dog would follow us — and hoping he wouldn't. The first hope had it. We'd barely gone halfway to the main road when we heard him — we felt his cold, wet, shoe-button nose

9

sniffling our legs. Peterkin was honorable about it. He turned and called back to Bill Monroe, watching us from the kitchen stoop, "Your hound-dog may follow us home. Hadn't you better call him back?"

The answer Bill gave us was the answer our ears were bursting to hear: "Doan't matter none to me where he goes so long's he's back by rabbit-huntin' season." That was the moment we knew we had a dog of our own — all legal — signed and sealed.

We waited until we were out of sight of the Monroes, then Peterkin asked, "He's got to have a name — seeing he's going to be ours for the whole summer. What will we call him?"

I turned and looked. There he was — looking almost as happy as we were. He had the funniest kind of a lope, his ears flopping and his nose still working hard at our smell as if he was making certain he would never lose us now he had found us. He ought to have the right sort of name — a name that would stick to him for keeps — as Peterkin and Snoodie stuck to us. I thought hard. "How about 'Daddles'?"

"'That's a silly name. You mean 'Dawdles'."

"No I don't. He doesn't dawdle and he doesn't wad-
dle. He daddles. Just look at him."

Peterkin looked. "All right for now, anyway. Maybe
later we'll think of a better one." But we never did,
and the name stuck.

When we reached the cottage Peterkin sang out,
"Mother — we've got some eggs for you!" The way he
said it you would have thought we had dozens. Mother
came out on the veranda, took one look at the basket

Peterkin was carrying, then she took a terribly long look at our dog. "Where did you get that stray dog? What I said last summer holds for this. No more strays."

"He's not a stray," I said. "He belongs to the Monroes — and Bill said we could keep him until rabbit season. That's a long way off."

We could see Mother was bothered. This was a different situation. Daddles knew something important was happening. He went up to the veranda steps, sat down, held up one paw and looked at Mother with those sad, beseeching eyes of his. I guess it was the eyes that did it. Mother just couldn't make them any sadder. "Well — " she said, and "Well — " again. And there she hesitated. "I guess you can keep him for a while — that is if he doesn't get tangled up with a skunk. Tell Jo she can feed him table scraps. But he's not to come into the house. That's final! If he is a Monroe dog he's bound to have fleas. I can't stand fleas."

What a day that was! First we tried Daddles out on retrieving sticks and tennis balls. Then we played badminton; and he brought back every cock we lost in the alder bushes, carrying it so carefully in his mouth not a feather was broken. In the afternoon we all three of us went up to the beech-woods back of Ben Butler's farm. It was our most favorite spot — this side of Bald Peak. We always came early in June to find a lady-slipper to bring to Mother and pick a few of the twin-flowers that grew down the slope near a small brook. You can talk all you like about three being a crowd. Peterkin, Daddles and I knew then that we made the finest company a dog and two children can ever know.

Of course Daddles didn't care a hoot about flowers; but those beech-woods must have been chockful of rabbit smells. We had barely found Mother's ladyslipper when Daddles was off like a flash, nose to the ground and baying like nobody's business. Peterkin and I sat down on a big fallen log and waited. It was fun. Daddles chased that rabbit clear around Bald Peak. A rabbit always doubles back on his trail. And soon we heard them coming back — Daddles's baying getting louder and louder. And then — before we knew it — there was the rabbit! Cute as a bug's ear! He was so surprised to see us he sat up straight, wriggled his whiskers and looked us straight in the eye. Daddles came along about

that time and he was as surprised as the rabbit. He had chased a rabbit right back to us — and all we'd done was look at him.

I suppose he expected us to shoot him and take him home to stew for dinner. Well — the rabbit jumped away into the far brush and Daddles came up to us and looked so disappointed that Peterkin and I tried our best to explain to him that we didn't shoot rabbits — or any other wild creature.

Jo gave Daddles a fine supper. She was our cook and we brought her down to Maine every summer. She liked dogs and she thought Daddles was wonderful. "Where's he going to sleep?" she asked. "I'll fix him an old blanket back of the kitchen stove."

We had to explain that Mother would not have him in the house. "She thinks he has fleas," we said.

"That fine gentleman of a dog have fleas! Never! But what your mother says goes. I'll get the blanket just the same. Maybe you childher can find a warmish spot under the alder bushes for him."

We tried our best to make him comfortable, patted him good-night and left him. But the next morning he was gone. Likely the Monroes were kinder to him than we had been and had given him a place to sleep back of their kitchen stove. June nights in Maine can be cold. Peterkin and I were terribly upset. But when we went up the lane to fetch the mail and supplies Ellis Freeman brought every morning — there was Daddles. He looked as pleased as we felt and daddled after us down the lane. Jo gave him a fine breakfast and we had another wonderful day.

But as dusk gathered we began to feel troubled. Jo called us into the kitchen and put fingers to lips. "I have thought of a way you childher could keep your dog. There be's an old market basket down cellar with two strong handles to it. Also a goodish length of old clothesline. Ye wait till the grown folks get settled in the other end of the house for the evening. Then open your window — whichever one you choose, let down the basket with the blanket folded at the bottom — and see if that dog doesn't like the idea."

"But Mother said we couldn't bring Daddles into the house. We can't disobey her." This from Peterkin.

Jo laughed — that throaty Irish laugh of hers. "But she never said a thing about your pulling him inside. She meant you were not to open the door and invite him to step inside. Faith, that's clear. You try the basket this night — and see what happens."

Jo made it sound so right that that's what we did. We waited until Mother had heard our prayers and tucked us in. Then we waited until our side of the house sounded quiet. We decided as Peterkin was the older he should have Daddles for the first night. We opened his window, pushed up the screen and lowered the basket. Then we called. We waited — then called again.

We had just about given up when we heard Daddles's low conversational whimper. "I'm coming," he was saying, "I'm coming." And sure enough, he reached the basket and walked around smelling it. Then he looked up at the window.

Peterkin called softly, "It's all right. Come along!" So — in he stepped, carefully, turned around three times and settled himself snugly at the bottom of the basket. We pulled it up, careful not to bump it against the side of the house. When it was even with the windowsill Daddles jumped inside. Then what a reuniting we had! Daddles licked us; we scratched and hugged him, all on Peterkin's bed. Then Peterkin lifted the comforter and

Daddles snuggled down underneath. I went back to my room and to bed, awfully happy. The next night it would be my turn to have Daddles.

After the first few days we settled down to regular doings. Jo took Daddles down when she went to get breakfast. She fed him properly on our kitchen stoop and then he went up the lane to wait for us by the mailbox. All our misgivings vanished like dandelion fluff in thin air. And supper for all of us grew happier and happier. During the day we hid the basket and rope in the back of Peterkin's closet where he kept his high rubber boots and his fishing tackle. Mother had agreed she would stop poking in it if Peterkin would promise to keep it tidy. So we felt safe.

It was still early June when Peterkin said Daddles ought to have a collar — just like any dog who really belonged to someone. "We can buy one out of our allowances," said Peterkin. I said, "No." We had all the August birthdays to keep and presents to buy for everyone. That would use up all our allowances. But I had a better idea.

"Look, Peterkin, we can pick blueberries this summer and sell them. Ellis Freeman will sell them in Belfast.

It wouldn't take too many quarts — not more than fifty."

Peterkin turned one of his handsprings — as he always did when he was pleased. "Good for you, Snoodie. We'll see Ellis Freeman tomorrow when he brings the mail." This we did. The three of us met the stage and told Ellis Freeman what we wanted to do. He was all for it — but not very encouraging.

"You young-uns'll be lucky to git ten cents a quart. My commission is two cents — that means you'll have to pick forty quarts if they come kinda scarce. If they come plentiful they's bring in less. You'll want a real good collar for that dog o' yourn."

After the stage left we all sat down at the head of the lane to think about it. The first thing we knew Daddles was bounding around us, barking like something wonderful had happened. Then he licked Peterkin and me and went bounding away down the lane — just as if everything was settled. And I guess it was. We knew then that no matter how hard the picking was and how long it took, Daddles was going to have his collar.

Only once in June did Mother repent and let Daddles come into the house. That was the night Ben Butler came down. He was one of our good neighbors and usually kept us supplied with eggs, chickens and vegetables. He came in, whooping loud as he always did. "Anybody at home? Kinda got a longin' for some sweet singing. Peterkin — Snoodie — you git out them gueetars and tune 'em up." He had brought Daddles in with him. When he caught Mother looking a bit doubt-

ful he added, quick-like, "He's a mighty well-behaved dog. Found him waiting outside. Kinda thought he might like some music — same as me."

Mother couldn't say a thing. She wouldn't hurt Ben Butler's feeling for anything. So we built up a big fire in the hall fireplace, brought out the hay-cushions and spread them round, then got our guitars and tuned them up. Ben liked anything we sang. I carried the tune and Peterkin was good at harmonizing. We sang all the college songs we knew — then the popular songs like "The Sidewalks of New York" and "The Bowery" — and finished up — as always — with spirituals. Daddles had settled himself between us and lay quiet as a lamb. But when we began "Old Black Joe" and "Roll, Jordan, Roll" Daddles sang along with us — the most whispering sad little singing you ever heard; but he never got badly off key. Afterwards we popped corn and Jo made hot cocoa.

Such a nice night, but when he left Ben Butler took Daddles with him and we didn't see him again for three days. When he came at last he looked starved — his ribs showed — and there was a frayed bit of rope about his neck, showing he'd been tied up by the Monroes and not fed. He got into the basket as if something hurt him; and when we got him inside on Peterkin's bed, we saw a horrid, ugly sore where the rope had cut into his neck. I got the Pond's Extract and Vaseline and tried to clean the sore and make it more comfortable. Daddles knew we were trying to help him — he was the knowingest dog we or the family had ever had. And the lovingest. I didn't know much about dog-healing, but I did know cleanness and care would help. It did, too. Next morning Jo seemed as upset about Daddles's ribs and sore as we were. "Such folks" (she meant the Monroes) "ought to be scalped by the Indians who used to live around here."

After that Daddles never missed a night — all summer. As soon as the blueberries started to ripen we began our picking; and then it was that William Henry Harrison Cox Sylvester Gerry Knight came to fix over one of our sitting rooms. We had two — one we really sat in, played games and read in, and one we kept more for company. When our parents were building the cottage all their friends in New York told Mother she should have one room finished off in burlap — you know, the stuff they make bags of. They kept telling Mother it was the latest thing — all the cottages at the seashore or in the mountains had one room finished off in burlap.

Well — Mother finally gave in and we had a sitting room we all hated. Father said it looked and smelled like a feed store. So after three years mother sent for William Henry Harrison Cox Sylvester Gerry Knight. That was his name. He lived out back — meaning back of the mountains — and he was the best all-round handy man in Knox and Waldo Counties. He could carpenter, plaster, paint, lathe, hang paper and build a chimney.

He arrived at seven-thirty sharp one morning and Peterkin, Daddles and I were on hand to welcome him. He drove a dingy mare named Nancy Hanks, harnessed to a cart that held everything — stepladder, pails, tools, sawhorses, boards, bags of stuff and a roll-up of clothing. He was small, wiry, with the cutest bunch of whiskers on his chin and the sharpest, most twinkling blue eyes you ever saw. We all liked him the moment he said "Whoa thar!" and came sliding off the cart. As he came closer we saw his lips were all puckered — as if a gathering string was inside; and all around was a brown circle. Later we found out this was caused by chewing tobacco. He handed out things for us to carry inside. Even Daddles carried his work-apron, made of blue-and-white ticking. By the time Mother came down for breakfast he had everything set up.

He was awfully polite, shaking Mother's hand and saying how pleased he was to be working for the Wymans. "Seems folks hereabouts think a heap of you, ma'm — even if you be summer-resorters. Got some rolls of real purty paper for you to choose from. Thar's jes' one thing I've forgot to fetch along."

"What's that?" asked Mother.

"Spittoon. I'm a chawin' man, and I cal'ated likely you'd have one handy yourself."

That was about the only time we ever saw Mother get flustered — or almost. But she didn't. She looked almost ashamed and said she was so sorry she didn't think that there was a spittoon in the house. I was about to speak up and say the Carletons had four in their store at the Harbor but W. H. H. C. S. G. Knight beat me to it. He said she needn't be bothered none about not having one — a bowl or a pot or something she could get along without would do just as well.

We stood around in absolute silence for a moment

and then Mother looked suddenly pleased as Punch. She turned to us. "You children remember the jardiniere your Aunt Emily sent as a present for the house? I think it's in the attic. That should do nicely. Do you think you two could bring it down — with the pedestal?"

Could we! Aunt Emily was the sort of person who was always giving to someone else what she didn't want. She wrote that it was a fine piece of majolica ware. We thought it was a fine piece of awfulness.

Peterkin and I lugged it down in no time and set it up. You should have seen William Henry Harrison Cox etcetera's eyes twinkle. "Handsomest thing I ever spit into, ma'm. I thank ye kindly." Then he set to work and it was a marvelous thing to watch him. He tore off the burlap and started nailing the lathes. In those days you had to have lathes to hold plaster. He filled his apron with lathes, one corner of his mouth with nails, the other with tobacco, climbed the ladder and began at the top. He would take out the nails, hammer three lathes into place and then spit. It was as regular as a clock ticking. He never chewed a nail or hammered the tobacco. Once in a while he would drop a lathe — then

Daddles would retrieve it and lift it up — his two front feet on the ladder — so Mr. Knight could reach it. He never spoke while he was doing one strip of lathes — only when he got to the floor and loaded up with his next batch of everything — lathes, nails and tobacco. "Smartest dog I ever see," he said. And when he broke off for lunch, by way of reward he gave Daddles a hunk of tobacco. That was one of the many times Daddles proved what a gentleman dog he really was. He took it, wagged his tail, and went to the door, waiting for Peterkin to open it. Then he disappeared. "Cal'ate that dog o' yourn doan't like good chawin' tobacco."

He looked almost hurt — so I said, "I think Daddles has taken it out to bury it where he buries his best bones. Most likely he'll enjoy it later."

The best sitting room was finally finished — the wood-work was all a soft ivory color, the wallpaper had a quiet pattern — just small pine branches and cones. William Henry Harrison Cox Sylvester Gerry Knight did it all in a week. He seemed as sorry to leave as we were to see him go. Mother gave him the jardiniere as a part-ing gift and he was so pleased he wanted to knock two dollars off his bill to show his appreciation. Of course

Mother wouldn't hear of it, so instead he offered, "Next time you want some work done I jes' as lief hash up with you Wymans as anyone else. Take the board money off your bill and make it a lot cheaper." Mother thanked him. We all liked William Henry Harrison

Cox Sylvester Gerry Knight a lot — even Mother; but I guess she didn't want him to "hash up" with us any more than she wanted Daddles around with his fleas — if he had any.

THE BLUEBERRIES were plentiful that summer. We spent long days on the ledges, picking as fast as we could, sometimes five quarts, sometimes more. Next morning we gave them to Ellis Freeman to sell. Ten cents a quart didn't last long. In two weeks the market was flooded and a quart of berries brought only eight cents. Peterkin and I felt awfully downdaunted; then Mr. Freeman cheered us up: "Seein' I be most as anxious for that hound-dog of yourn to git a collar as you be I doan't aim to charge you young-uns any commission. You'll be gittin' eight cents straight fer all you pick."

Well — that started us picking longer and harder. The day we filled a ten-quart pail made the last. Ellis Freeman chuckled mightily when we handed it over next morning. "Seems like that ought to make sartin sure enough to buy the finest collar in Belfast." He handed us our mail but he didn't start the stage. Just sat looking at us. Then he chuckled again. "Seems like you young-uns should ride up to Belfast with me and pick out the collar yourselves. Be up prompt tomorrow mornin', and it won't cost you a cent."

"Can Daddles go?" I asked.

"Sartin sure!"

Peterkin turned cartwheels almost all the way down the lane, and Daddles acted plain crazy with delight. As for me — I tried a cartwheel and couldn't do it; so I just skipped after the others and whooped with joy.

We marked the next day with a red circle on our calendar. Mother said we could go and gave us some money so we could invite Ellis Freeman to have noon-dinner with us. We were up the lane a half-hour before the stage got there the next morning. The three of us climbed into the front seat of the surrey with Ellis and off we went. That day we really found out what a wonderful man our stage driver was. We watched him jog-trot up to the houses to deliver something special

or take in all the stuff the farmers along the road wanted him to sell in Belfast. Ellis Freeman never walked. He never got tired. He never wrote down a single thing he took to sell or what he was to buy with the money it brought. And he never made a mistake. There were a pair of fryers to sell and carpet slippers to buy; there were a bushel of peas and five yards of blue-and-white calico, rickrack braid and cotton thread to buy; there were a basket of clams and three pounds of flounder-fillets to sell and in return six pillowcases and as many hand-towels as there was money left. So it went. Ellis let Peterkin and me deliver the mail on our side of the road; and when he had to get out of the stage we held the horses. It was fun.

Halfway there a farmer's wife by the name of Nichols gave him fifteen quarts of berries to sell. In return she wanted a bonnet, natural straw, with blue flowers on it. She favored bachelor's-buttons. As we started off again I asked Ellis Freeman how he dared buy a hat for a woman. He chuckled. "Snoodie, seems like I can please 'em more than they can please themselves. It's this-a-way. They git into a millinery shop with hundreds of bonnets to look at — all colors — all shapes. They hain't able to make up their minds to which bonnet to buy. Likely they'll end up choosin' one that doan't favor them none. So they come home disappointed. That's the way it goes."

Peterkin and I thought Belfast quite a city. It had some lovely old white houses, lots of shops; and the streets were crowded with carts, buggies, buckboards and bicycles. We left the stage at the livery stable so the horses could rest and be fed. Ellis gave me and Peterkin baskets and we all went out to sell and to buy. Daddles tagged right behind us, as excited as we were. Sometimes Ellis bargained — to get more money for some things or pay less for what he had to buy. In the millinery shop we had to take a bonnet with cornflowers, but they were a lovely blue so I guessed it would turn out all right.

Then we had dinner at Mr. Freeman's favorite "chophouse." He took a boiled dinner and Peterkin and I took a shore dinner. The waitress took Daddles into the kitchen and fed him — no charge — and we all ended up with blueberry pie, even Daddles. After that we went to a harness-maker whom Mr. Freeman knew and who made the best collars in Belfast. He tried on several and we settled for a nice soft black one with a nickel plate on it for a name. Then we were shooed out to do some window-shopping while Ellis Freeman paid for the collar and took it to have it engraved. He'd said he thought he better — once it was marked he didn't "cal'ate" any white trash — names not mentioned — would "darst" to sell it.

Daddles wore his collar going home. He sat up so proud on the front seat, between Peterkin and me. Mrs. Nichols was pleased as Punch with her bonnet. She had to try it on right there so we all could admire it. Everyone was pleased with what we had bought for them. Ellis gave back the change — if there was any — and everything was settled fair and square. He never made a mistake; and as I said before — not a thing written down. So we got home at last, awfully tired and awfully happy.

I haven't told you about our candle-table in the upstairs hall. There was no electricity in those days. In the cottage we had kerosene lamps, but for going to bed we all had candles. In the big upstairs sitting-room-hall, against the wall, stood our candle-table —

everyone had his own candle. We were supposed to light them and carefully douse the match in the mug of water that was there, so as to be sure we started no fires. Mother was especially afraid of fire. Once started our cottage would burn like tinder, Mother said.

Soon after Daddles got his collar we had one of our regular guests come for a visit, a professor from Harvard. We all liked him a lot. One night as we were all going to bed early after a day of fishing, Professor Gage said our candle-table always put him in mind of Hanukkah, the Jewish Feast of Lights. Peterkin and I had never heard of it and we asked him to tell us more. He said it came about the same time as our Christmas. Every Jewish home lighted special candles, but they lighted them from a servant-candle.

We liked the idea a lot. Peterkin asked would it be sacrilegious if we had a servant-candle to light ours at night. Well — Professor Gage said he didn't think so — if we did it in the right way. The next morning the grownups drove to Camden to do some shopping and our professor bought us a sort of servant-candle. It was a fat candle, under a globe of red glass and set on a nickel-plated dish with a handle. We were pleased, and that night when we went up to bed our professor made a little ceremony out of the lighting of Peterkin's and my candles. He said what he could remember of what was said at Hanukkah in every Jewish home. I liked it so much I remembered some of it. It went like this:

> The candle that gives its light to others is the servant-candle.
> A candle is a small thing but it can light another.
> You are such a light.
> You can help to move back the darkness in the world.
> You can help to kindle the hearts of others.

Two nights afterward we had our fire.

I guess our servant-candle was something like a hurricane light. Mother had warned us to be sure after we had lighted our candles to put back the glass globe. Well, that night somebody probably forgot to do that. We children had gone to bed early. It was the night for Daddles to sleep with Peterkin. We were fast asleep when Daddles must have smelled smoke. He crawled out from under the comforter and began licking Peterkin's face. Then he pulled at the bedclothes; and finally he began to bark. That really waked Peterkin — and he smelled the smoke. He and Daddles were out in the hall in a jiffy.

The windows were all open and a stiff wind was blowing. It had blown the cotton spread on the candle-table over the servant-candle. It was burning fast. The wood of the table was scorched almost black and the wallpaper back of the table was burning. While Peterkin ran to get water in the pail that always stood in the bathroom Daddles went from door to door — baying louder and louder.

I was out next and called "Fire! Fire!" as I helped Peterkin lug the pail and douse the flames. Soon the hall was full of sleepy people, all asking questions at once. By that time the fire danger was over — but it looked an awful mess. Somebody closed the windows. Peterkin, Daddles and I crawled up on the window seat and began to giggle. All the grownups had come running in all sorts of night gear: nightgowns, night-shirts and just blankets wrapped around them. They did look funny. Only our professor came properly at-tired in a dressing gown over whatever he wore to sleep in. The red-glass globe was shattered in a hun-

dred pieces and was all over the floor. Mother asked
Peterkin to get a brush and dustpan and sweep it up
before anyone got cut. It was then that she really saw
Daddles.

"Where did that dog come from?" She sounded very
stern — as she always did when she thought we had
broken one of her rules. Peterkin and I looked at each
other. I guess we knew then that our game of basket
and clothesline and smuggling in Daddles was over.

I spoke up first. "You're all wrong about Daddles
having fleas. We bought a fine-toothed comb in Belfast and combed him well — and found only one flea!"

"How did that dog get inside?" This time Mother
looked and sounded even sterner.

Peterkin tried next. "Look, Mother — if Daddles
hadn't been inside tonight we would all probably have
burned up. He was the first to smell the smoke. He
woke me up — and all the rest of you. He probably
saved our lives."

"All right. But I want to know how that dog got
inside to smell the smoke; how did he get in your room
to wake you up? Maybe he did save us all from burning up but I want to know how he got inside to do it."

Peterkin and I looked at each other — then at Mother. Mother looked as accusing as a court judge. We knew then that we would have to tell everything. We owned up to the basket and clothesline, to taking turns at the window and to which one would have Daddles for the night. When we finished we thought doomsday was about to descend upon us. Then Jo saved us. None of us had heard her come down from her room upstairs, not until she spoke. "I'll not have the childher blamed for Daddles, ma'm. I put the notion in their heads. 'Twas I got them the basket and blanket and all. So you can blame me entirely."

For a moment everyone sat still and stony — just as if they were petrified. Then Mother started to laugh. One of the things we loved about Mother was her sense of fun and how much she liked a good joke. Soon everyone was laughing. We were shooed off to bed and no one said a word about Daddles. And from that day forth — Mother never called him "that dog."

Two days later I came down with scarlet fever.

I was awfully sick, I guess. Dr. Hart came up every day to see me and only Mother was allowed in my room. My throat was very sore and the fever made my mind all blurry. The spots on me were so scarlet you could hardly see any white. A sheet wrung out in carbolic solution was hung over the door. Through the day Mother sopped my face with Pond's Extract, but the nights were the worst. I kept asking for Daddles — asking and asking. Funny how things get all woven together when you have a bad fever. You never know when something begins and when it ends. I kept asking and asking and then — suddenly — there was Daddles. I put my hand down under the light blanket and felt his cold nose. Then he gave my fingers a lick. I tried opening my eyes to see if it was nighttime. And there on my dressing table was another servant-candle, just like the one that was broken in the fire. Its glowing red eye seemed to say: "Get well, Snoodie, get well."

After that everything seemed better. I learned afterwards that in the daytime Peterkin had Daddles; but Mother had to scrub him off with carbolic solution. Daddles, I mean. He must have hated that. When I started to get well I got well fast. It was the peeling that took so long. Dr. Hart said I couldn't come out of quarantine until I had lost all the old skin. Mother cut my hair close, and rubbed me over with carbolic

Vaseline from scalp to toes. It made me smell something awful. Only Daddles stood it like a hero. He must have hated it worse than the baths he got each morning. I helped the job of peeling along but I did feel like a shedder lobster, getting rid of his old shell.

Two or three times during the day Peterkin and Daddles would stand on the outside of the sheet and call, "Feeling better, Snoodie?" and I would always answer, "Much better." It did please me to have Peterkin care.

When I first started to walk again I was still weak and my legs buckled under me. I went down just like a folding campstool. But soon I was navigating all right. Days that were sunny and warm enough we three spent under the big white birch by the cottage. Jo brought us our lunch there, and we made two new friends. One was a redstart, the friendliest of all the warblers. The other was a chipmunk. What really brought him to us was his stomach. Jo made orange marmalade sandwiches sometimes and that chipmunk went completely crazy over orange marmalade. He could smell it in the air as soon as Jo came out. We could hear him coming, lickety-split, chattering as he came.

Then rabbit season began and Daddles had to go back to the Monroes. Peterkin took him and left him. But he came back for one more night. You would never guess what brought him.

Perhaps you remember about our going in June to the beech-woods and how Daddles hunted a rabbit for us and was so disgusted because we didn't shoot him? That must have weighed on his mind all summer, for two nights before we were leaving Haddock Harbor it happened.

We had given up expecting to see Daddles again. As we were going to bed Peterkin said, "I guess we better put the basket and clothesline away for good, Snoodie." I agreed. Then I thought better: "Let's put it down one more night. Daddles might come back to say good-by."

So we lowered the basket from Peterkin's window — expecting nothing. We heard it go *kerplunk* on the ground. Then we waited. There was a fine half-moon in the sky and the stars were spangled everywhere. The air was keen and cooling and we gulped it in, making a lot of noise. We stopped a second, and then we heard it — a sort of shooshing sound. It came from the alders. So Peterkin and I stuck out our heads to see better. There was Daddles. But instead of coming daddling quickly to the basket he was tugging and pulling and tugging something. He reached the basket at last. But instead of getting in himself he looked up at the window, whimpered a little and starting tugging and pulling again until he had what he was lugging inside the basket. Then he sat down, whimpering some more, and saying as plainly as anything, "Now you pull it up."

We did. The basket seemed almost as heavy as if

Daddles was in it. When it was even with the windowsill we looked inside. There was a dead rabbit. He must have hunted, killed and brought it to us all that long distance from the beech-woods. He had thought it all out — we hadn't wits enough to get a rabbit for ourselves so he must get one for us. We lowered the basket again for Daddles and when he got inside Peterkin's room he bounced around, splitting his sides with delight.

The rabbit didn't sleep with us that night. Peterkin took it down cellar. We showed it to Jo next morning and she agreed she must make it into a potpie. Nobody ate much, so Daddles had a real feast. He stayed with us all day and that night, so I had him to sleep on my bed once more. Next day we left. Daddles followed the stage all the way to the Monroes. The last we saw of him before the road took us out of sight he was sitting on the edge of the grass, one paw up, wishing us good-by.

We hated to leave him behind but we weren't sad. We knew — knew for sure — we would be having another lovely summer, all three of us together, next year. And we did.

W E CAME BACK early the next summer. Apple blossoms, pines and salt sea were in the air again. It was good to see Ellis Freeman on the dock waiting as the old *Lewiston* tied up. His tongue was spilling over as always with Haddock Harbor gossip. But what we wanted most to hear was news of Daddles. Our stage driver chuckled mightily as he told about him: "That plain hound-dog o' yourn must have known you were comin'. He's been sittin' in your lane, waiting for ye, for the last five days."

And there he was! Peterkin hardly waited for the stage to stop, and I was close after him. We jumped. The next moment we were rolling on the grass; and I guess you couldn't have told which was Peterkin, Daddles or me. We hugged and got licked and forgot entirely that we had on our city clothes. For once Mother said nothing, and we went pelting down the lane ahead of the stage. It wasn't until we got to the cottage that we really took a good look at Daddles. He had his collar and he didn't look as thin as he had when we got him last summer. I guess the Monroes had really treated him with more kindness.

Eggs were plentiful again so we had no egg-trouble. We visited the beech-woods and brought Mother her annual spring ladyslipper; we watched for the wild strawberries to ripen. Never had the Wymans had so much shortcake and wild strawberry ice cream as we had that summer. Mother made us little picking measures out of birch bark. They had loops we could string a belt or cord through to tie around our waists to leave both hands free to pick and hull. The sea-meadows were chockful of berries that late June. Daddles would lie under a bush while we picked. But he always kept one eye open. If he had been glad to be with us the summer before he was twice as glad — twice as devoted — this year. So were we.

I guess we all liked our feelings in those sea-meadows,

picking berries. We loved to watch the gulls, swooping nearby: sea gulls, black-backs, terns and mackerel gulls. We loved to watch the schooners go by — up the Penobscot to Bangor. Two-, three-, even four- and five-masters. There isn't a prettier thing on the water than a schooner in full sail. Sometimes a square-rigger came — a bark or a barkentine. A day was to come when we watched a six-master launched from the Camden shipyards.

Always before Peterkin and I had thought picking berries was a chore, but with Daddles along we loved it. When wild raspberry time came Daddles seemed to know just where they were thickest. You find them best in some wood-clearing, where the slash has been piled and burned. We just followed Daddles, and sure enough, give him time and he would lead us to a spot on the mountains where they were big and ripe and slathers of them — as they say in Maine.

On those wood-days we found more than raspberries. We were always running into interesting things. One day we saw a hen-partridge; the bird books call them rough grouse. She went down the path ahead of us, trailing a wing as if it was broken. We knew it wasn't. She was just leading us away from her nest. When she thought she had decoyed us far enough off she flew with a whirring of wings and we went back and found the nest. It had a clutch of four eggs — the prettiest things. We touched nothing. Even Daddles understood and didn't smell them. Another time we discovered a brood of young partridges, just hatched out. They looked like small brown leghorn chicks. It was fun to watch Daddles nuzzle them. One he picked up very gently and brought to us. We made him put it down and then we left — hoping we hadn't left too strong a smell of human beings and dog behind us.

Several times we dared the black flies and went trout fishing. We did it the simple way — no fancy flies or tackle. The best holes were along the Four Corner Brook. We started out with just a rough hunk of wood with fish-line on it, some homemade flies, split shot, and Peterkin brought his claspknife. When we got to the brook Peterkin cut a stretch of straight alder. At the ends we fastened our lines, added a couple of shot to weight it so we could cast well, tied on our flies. Then Peterkin cut a crotch of alder to string the trout we caught. We took turns at the best holes. Daddles had never been brook trout fishing before but he caught on fast. He kept at our heels, and never barked until we had pulled the trout safely to land. Then he made a general whoopee with us, especially if it was a big trout.

It was pretty fishing. The brook was edged with fern and birch and sassafras and shadbush. The rocks had different kinds of moss. There were lots of birds, warblers, nuthatches and thrushes. Ever catch a speckled beauty of a trout while a hermit thrush sang? Well —

it's something you always remember. You fish along the side of the brook that does not have the sun back of you — so it can't cast your shadow across the pool. That scares trout; so does noise, like cracking twigs and rolling stones. Jo always put us up a good lunch, and we picked the prettiest spot to eat it in. And when we were thirsty we just scooped up the brook-water — all spring-fed — and drank. As I said, we liked things best when we could keep them simple. At the end of the day we could throw away our alder-poles, wind up our lines and start homeward. Once we got within calling distance of the cottage Peterkin always sang out, "Hi, Mother, come see! Trout enough for dinner."

In those days there was good salmon fishing along the Penobscot. Ben Butler had a berth off his shore where he strung his nets. We had one off ours; but as we couldn't use it we gave it to Ben Butler. He wanted to pay Mother something for it, but she wouldn't listen. So three times during the salmon season — June through July — Ben Butler brought us half a salmon. He always brought us one for the Fourth of July. Salmon, fresh garden peas, wild strawberry shortcake are as much a part of a Maine Fourth as firecrackers and fireworks used to be.

He brought it this time the day before the Fourth and he looked terribly worried. Mother noticed this. After she had thanked him, she asked if the salmon weren't running well this season.

"Never better. 'T hain't that," said Ben. "A lot worse. This season someun is stealin' 'em. Takes my boat in the dead of night and takes every durned fish the nets have caught. Must have taken a dozen salmon so fur — goldurn him!" We had never heard Ben Butler swear before.

Mother wanted to pay for the salmon this time, but Ben wouldn't let her. "What are you going to do? You can't let him go on stealing," said Mother.

"Aim to set up and wait fur him. I'll take along my shotgun so as to be sure and wing him if he takes to runnin'."

Peterkin looked at me and I looked at him. We'd never had a chance to help catch a salmon thief before. So we walked a piece with Ben up the lane. "When are you going to watch for him?" asked Peterkin.

Ben Butler pulled his thinking-lock. "Tonight, meb-be. Might as well make it kind a celebration for the Fourth — afore I lose any more fish."

"Think we could come along — Snoodie, me and Daddles? A hound-dog might come in handy," said Peterkin.

"What would your mother think?"

Peterkin winked at Ben Butler — man to man. "She needn't know, need she? Then she wouldn't worry. She lets Snoodie and me go out with you when you pull the nets. Seems only fair we should go along when you catch whoever is stealing your salmon. We can tell her tomorrow. Please, Ben!"

Ben pulled his thinking-lock hard. "Doan't seem right. Your mumma's a fair and square woman. Seems like we should be fair and square with her. You ask her first. Tell her I'd be mighty glad to have you young-uns along."

I spoke up then. "She might think it was dangerous. It wouldn't be — would it?"

"By gosh, no. Safe as berry-pickin'. I cal'ate who-somever's stealin' the fish feels purty sure I won't be stayin' up o' nights to catch him. He's just some no-account rascal, livin' not too fur off and thinkin' it's a mighty easy way to make a few dollars."

"But you said you were taking your shotgun. He might have one too." I wasn't scared, but I did want to know how much reason our mother might have to be scared for us.

Ben Butler shook his head hard. "Not a chance. You see, Snoodie, if he fetched a gun along and was caught with it — and the fish too — he'd be compoundin' a felony. Know what I mean? All I'm takin' along my gun fur is to keep him from runnin'. If I catch him stealin' I want to scare the daylights out of him. See what I mean?"

We did, but would Mother see it our way? By this time Ben, Daddles, Peterkin and I had reached the head of the lane. We knew it was up to Ben to decide, and we were hoping awfully hard he would decide to let us come. Even Daddles sat there, hoping. You could tell he cared a lot by the way he hunched up his ears and wagged his tail and looked with a lot of beseeching at Ben. And then — all in a minute we knew we had won. Ben was grinning. "Seems like your mumma has trusted you young-uns to me a lot. She's let me take you fishin' and net-haulin' and stakin' out lobster pots. And that time — two winters ago, when you were a mighty puny-lookin' pair, she took you out of school and sent you down to Betsy Eliza and me to look after till summer come. By gosh, by golly, I cal'ate she won't mind none your comin' along tonight. Only you've got to promise you'll tell her tomorrow."

We swore and Daddles yapped twice; and the three of us pelted down the lane — happy as if we'd all three been hound-dogs, instead of just Daddles.

Before night came Peterkin and I were bursting our seams with excitement; even Daddles knew something was afoot. We undressed, let Mother tuck us up as always, then we did some more waiting. Everyone had lighted his candle and gone to his room before we dared dress again. Like always we had pulled Daddles up, this time from Peterkin's window. I waited for them to come for me and the three of us, no, two of us carrying our shoes tiptoed down the stairs, with the third of us, having no shoes to carry, going as softly as if he were one of our shadows.

Peterkin said we better not go by the shore; so we

crossed the meadows to Ben Butler's garden, then went down the path to his boathouse. He was waiting for us, inside. "See you made it," said he, looking pleased. "Think I'll be kinda glad to have company. Still got a whale of a lot of night afore us."

Ben brought up lobster traps for Peterkin and me to sit on. He laid a pile of burlap bags on the floor for Daddles. Then he sat down again, his shotgun across his knees, and the waiting began.

Sometimes we whispered a little, but mostly we listened. It seemed as if a hundred small stones rolled themselves along the beach; it seemed as if a thousand dry twigs snapped along the path. The tide was almost low when we got there, coming in. It was half-tide; and I know I was thinking this wasn't going to be the night for salmon-stealing. And then it happened. Ben Butler had left the door of the boathouse open a crack. I was beginning to yawn — a long, loud yawn, when we heard steps, plain, following the path. All of us held our breaths. A figure passed the crack in the door. It stopped to pick up the oars Ben always left standing outside. In a moment we could hear the boat being pushed down the slip, and the splash it made when it hit the water. Ben reached forward and swung the door wider open. We could see the figure more distinctly then. He wore an old hat, pulled down on his head, and a bulgy short jacket. I had kept still as long as I could. If I wasn't going to burst all my seams I had to speak. "Aren't you going to catch him before he steals any more?" I whispered of course, but my voice sounded awfully loud in the stillness.

When Ben spoke he, too, sounded loud. "Hain't got no case against him till we catch him with a fish. Got to wait a while longer."

And wait we did. We watched as the thief rowed out to the pound. We saw him catch hold of the nets, take up Ben's gaff, and then we saw the splash of the first salmon. Daddles had risen the moment the figure passed the boathouse door. Peterkin held him now, as his hackles rose and low growls came out while he shook and shook under Peterkin's hand. I guess we all began to shake. The thief got three salmon out of Ben's nets then he rowed on to the ones off our shore.

There was an old moon that night, but plenty of clouds. Every time the moon slipped out clear of them we saw a splash. He, the thief, must have taken at least three more salmon. We could see every splash plainly for the water sparkled with phosphorescence. If I hadn't been so excited and a little scared I would have thought what a pretty sight it was to watch. We could almost see the pinky sheen on the salmon scales.

The moon went under the clouds as the thief rowed back, landed in the slip and hauled the boat up. By this time Daddles was splitting his seams. Peterkin held him with one hand and cupped the other hand over his mouth to keep back the growls. He kept saying, "Quiet, Daddles, it's not time yet."

But for Daddles the time came sooner than we expected. It was nearly full-tide now. The thief jerked the boat above high-water mark, then started to take out the salmon and lay them, tidy, on a big flat rock. We had counted six when Daddles bolted. He was bursting with growlings and bayings as he sprang and caught the end of the man's coat in his teeth, and hung on. This knocked the hat off the thief's head. We could see his face plainly then — and who should it be but Bill Monroe!

Ben was on his feet, his shotgun slung ready; Peterkin and I were close behind. But we were not in time

to save Daddles. Bill Monroe tore him loose from his coat and as he sprang again gave him a terrible kick. Daddles must have been all of six feet in the air before he landed. I didn't reach much higher than Bill Monroe's chest, but I could have sprung then for his throat and throttled him. But Ben gripped me tight. "Go easy, Snoodie, we'll make him pay for that." He swung with the butt end of his gun across Bill Monroe's legs and sent him sprawling on the rocks. Ben drawled on, "Good haul you made this time. Cal'ate we got a clear case against you for stealin' salmon."

I can never remember all the things that happened next. Bill began stuttering something about paying back for all the salmon he'd taken — if he was given time. Daddles came crawling slowly back to me and Peterkin, and Ben said having Bill arrested was too good treatment for a man as mean and sneaking as he was. How it would have ended if Peterkin hadn't spoken up I don't know. But Peterkin did and I thought everything was going to blow sky-high. "You don't deserve to own a fine dog like Daddles — steal your neighbor's salmon and then have your own dog catch you at it. Sell him to us and we'll pay any price you ask."

That did it! Bill Monroe had gotten to his feet. Daddles was halfway over to where we were. Then, quick like a flash of lightning, Bill raised his foot to kick Daddles again. That kick could have finished the dog we loved so much and who loved us; and Peterkin would have always felt the blame for it — if it had happened. But Ben Butler saved the day, or the dawn, I guess. This time he used the barrel of his shotgun. How he did it I never knew; but he sprayed a blast of bird shot into Bill Monroe's farther leg and missed Daddles. I grabbed him. Bill let out an awful yelp and swore like a pirate. He made one last try to snatch Daddles from me but Ben Butler roared at him, "You leave that dog be! And you quit stealin' salmon or I'll have the full heft of law on you."

That finished it. Bill Monroe went limping home. He wore heavy hip boots and I guess he was more scared than hurt. The rest of us went our separate ways. Peterkin took Daddles and carried him home. He was awfully bruised. We felt him over carefully when we finally got him on Peterkin's bed, but we didn't think any bones were broken. He whimpered and licked our fingers as we probed. We brought him food, but he wouldn't touch it. Just as day really broke we got into bed — tuckered out but so thankful we had Daddles home safe with us.

Next day Ben Butler went to the Harbor to ship his salmon to Boston and he couldn't keep from telling everyone what had happened. Mother had to do some errands early that day and so she knew what happened from old Cap'n Calderwood: "I cal'ate you heard how your young-uns along with that hound-dog and Ben Butler caught Bill Monroe robbin' the nets off your shore an' his. Kinda a good joke — to have his own dog catch him thievin', hain't it?"

It was lucky for us Mother liked a good joke. The moment she got back we knew she knew. She tried to look stern but couldn't quite. "So that's why you've been carrying Daddles around all day! Supposing you tell me just what happened, and next time I would rather hear such doings from my children than pick it up as Harbor gossip."

Peterkin owned up that we were afraid she wouldn't let us go if we asked her. I said, "You let us go out with Ben Butler when he pulls his nets and we eat some of the salmon he catches. It seemed only right we should help him catch the thief."

What Mother really thought about it we never knew — that's a way with mothers. But she didn't put us on bread and water and she didn't take our allowances away.

We had one more kind of fishing that summer. The mackerel came into the Harbor and all three of us had a wonderful time catching them. At least Peterkin and I did. I guess Daddles would have told another tale — if he could have. But he went along every time — fair weather or foul.

Did you ever get up at crack of dawn — get your own breakfast and row out a good nautical mile into Penobscot Bay to watch the sun come up while you wait for a school of mackerel to swim near enough to be caught? It is a time full of wonder.

Peterkin always got up first — then called me. He had a fire started and bacon frying by the time I came down. I made toast while he fried the eggs. Daddles had just what we had — except the toast and marmalade. And how he licked up his piece of lemon me-

ringue pie that Jo always made for us. We all said it
brought us luck.

Daddles wasn't as good a sailor as Peterkin or me.
We took Ben Butler's boat — he was always glad to
lend it. Usually it was still dark with just a crack of

orange showing in the east when we got out far enough. It was too deep to drop anchor, but Peterkin had rigged up a sea-anchor that kept us from drifting much. Usually it was as calm as a millpond when we first got out, but soon an offshore breeze sprang up and made the bay choppy. Then Daddles's trouble began. It was helped, I guess by the toll-bait we had. Toll-bait is made of old stale fish, clams, anything that smells a lot. You chop it up and then dish it overboard. It spreads over the top of the water and lures the mackerel in. As soon as a big school is around the boat you throw out two lines each, no bait, and weighted only with mackerel-jigs. When they begin to bite you haul them in, one line after another, as fast as you can. You don't even have to unhook a mackerel — just flip the line and he drops off into your box or basket.

As I have said, the toll-bait added to Daddles's trouble. And I guess the big piece of lemon pie for breakfast wasn't too good. Anyway he tried his best. He hung his head way over the gunwale of the boat; and when Peterkin shouted at him, "Please, Daddles — turn your head away!" he tried awfully hard.

It wasn't just catching mackerel that made those

dawns red-letter days for us. It was like watching the world being created anew to watch the sun come up — the orange streak changing to flames — orange, yellow, crimson; to watch the whole bay catch the glory of it — to watch the western sky take fire. People who don't ever watch sunrises miss a lot of wonder.

One morning we caught so many mackerel we almost sank the boat. Luckily for us there wasn't much wind that day. Peterkin rowed and I kept the boat balanced and we got safely to Ben Butler's slip. We loaded his wheelbarrow with the fish, and when we got to the house there was Mother, waiting. We thought it was pretty nice of Mother to let us go out on the water as often as we did — for you see she hated it herself. I guess she was really scared of it. But she never said so. This morning when she saw all the mackerel she smiled and said what a jolly good time we must have had, and hadn't we better give the fish away to anyone at the Harbor who could use them.

So we did. We had lots of fun; and Daddles liked peddling the mackerel better than catching them. Nearly everyone took six to a dozen; and we all got handouts. Daddles enjoyed the handouts as much as we did. There was pie at Gramma Snow's and doughnuts and milk at the Pendletons; and when we got to the Butlers there was the last of one of Betsy Eliza's cream-cakes. They were always wonderful: three layers with real whipped cream between them. To watch Daddles lick down his piece you would never have thought he had lost a good breakfast and piece of lemon pie not so long ago.

THE AUGUST of that second summer the circus came to Camden. It was a country circus — one ring and tents, and I expect most people would have thought it couldn't compare with the Barnum and Bailey Circus that came every year to Madison Square Garden. But Peterkin and I liked it better.

The Butlers invited us, all expenses paid. They had never been to a circus and I guess they were even more excited than we were. The day before we had a sort of argument with Ben and Betsy Eliza about taking Daddles. They didn't think a circus was any place for him. He might tangle with a tiger or lion, or he might get lost in the crowd. But we thought it wasn't fair to leave him behind because it was going to be such a special day for all of us. In the end the Butlers gave in.

Ben Butler didn't intend to miss any part of the circus — neither parade, sideshows nor the performance. So he had us down for breakfast at seven o'clock. Betsy Eliza had a first-class meal for us: salt-pork and milk gravy; hot biscuits; sauce, two kinds; pie, three kinds; doughnuts; milk for us and coffee for them. She had it all ready when we got there. The kitchen table was spread with a red-and-white checked cloth.

She must have spent all the day before cooking for our picnic dinner. While I helped dry and put away breakfast dishes Peterkin went out to the barn with Ben to help harness up.

We were off long before nine in what the Butlers called "the wagon." It had two seats, no fringed top like a surrey, but lots of room to stow away things under the seats. We drove behind Maude, the mare, a spanking young trotter. I always thought only mules were called Maude; but Ben said it was a good name for a mare. We were in Camden at the fairgrounds an hour before the parade began.

Peterkin and I never knew whether we had more fun

out of our own enjoyment or watching the others —
their first time at a circus. Ben liked the lady bareback
rider in spangles best; Betsy Eliza liked best the trained
horses; Peterkin and I liked best the clowns — they
were wonderful and spilling over with jokes and fun.
Daddles liked everything. After the parade we visited
the cages and the elephants. There was one special one
— a big old elephant — that kind of hypnotized Daddles. He kept walking round and round it — trying to
make out which was front and which was back. Suddenly, before we could grab him, he got too close. In
the wink of an eye the elephant had picked up Daddles
in his trunk and was swinging him back and forth. We
were scared. It looked as if at any moment he might
let go and pitch Daddles over the heads of the crowd
into the field beyond. Or he might open his big mouth
and swallow him whole. Daddles never let out a whimper, and the crowd said, "Now isn't that cute!" If Daddles had been their dog they wouldn't have seen anything cute about what was happening.

How long it went on I don't know — it seemed
years. Peterkin pulled a handful of peanuts out of his
pocket and offered them in exchange. I kept looking at

the elephant. He didn't look mean — not as if he would hurt anything as small as a dog. And all Daddles had done was walk round and round him — never barking, never even nuzzling him. At last he put him down gently and we gave him all our peanuts. I guess he was just having fun. It must be awfully stupid standing most of the day, hitched to a big stake with a chain around your leg, having people gawk at you.

Once on the ground Daddles came running to us. Peterkin picked him up; and the rest of the day he carried him everywhere. After that we found a piece of meadow with a wide-spreading maple tree for shade, and had our lunch. It was a humdinger: cold chicken, potato salad, biscuits wrapped up so thick they were still warmish. Butter and jam, cookies; but the best of all was Betsy Eliza's cream-cake — three layers thick. Even Daddles forgot his troubles when he ate chicken and cream-cake. Ben got hot coffee for himself and Betsy Eliza and Moxie for us. We begged a pan and some water for Daddles from the tattooed lady. She had a cart that she lived in and she liked dogs.

All the sideshows were good. And the circus itself

was wonderful. With only one ring, you never missed a trick. The clowns visited with all the children and pulled all-day suckers out of little girls' curls and boys' pants pockets. Ben Butler wanted to buy us all pink lemonade and spun-sugar candy. Every bench was filled and lots of people were standing. There was fun everywhere. The performers seemed to be having as good a time as we were. That's the way a circus ought to be. When it was over Peterkin put Daddles down — to stretch his legs and rest his own arms. Of course the crowd was heaving, pushing its way out of the tent; and when we got outside Daddles was gone — lost.

We called and called. We hunted and hunted. We visited all the sideshows and even asked the tattooed lady had she seen him. We hung around the elephants — but no Daddles. With all his chores to do Ben Butler at last said he was sorry but we'd have to go home. It was the saddest ending to a wonderful day.

Peterkin and I couldn't eat any supper. Jo tried to cheer us up: "Let the two of ye stop being downdaunted. 'Tis plain what happened. That Daddles followed the wrong pair of childher out of the tent. He's a knowledgeable dog. By the time he got a good smell of them he followed he knew his mistake. He'll be taking the right road home — and soon — see if he doesn't."

But he didn't come. Peterkin and I couldn't get to sleep, thinking of all the possible things that might have happened. Three nights we put down the basket for him, watched and waited. Jo kept a good dinner waiting for him. But he didn't come. On the fourth night we put down the basket again; and we finally left it on the ground under Peterkin's window — fastening the clothesline well. We sat on the edge of Peterkin's bed. For the first time I began to cry — and I was almost blubbering. Ben Butler had been right — a circus was no place for a small dog. We were the ones to blame for having taken him. Now if anything had happened to him it was our fault. I knew then how terrible it was to find out what it was like to have something happen to anyone you loved — as much as we loved Daddles — and know it was your fault.

"We'll never have another dog we love so much," said I. "Oh, Peterkin, you don't think anyone would really hurt him, do you?"

Peterkin was wonderful. He wiped his nose and did

his best to comfort me like a big brother. I forget what he said because we suddenly heard a sound outside the open window. "Listen," said Peterkin. Then we heard it plain as always — Daddles's low whimpering — telling Peterkin and me he had come home.

We pulled him up and then we were racing all over the house shouting, "Daddles is safe! Come see!" and everyone came — the family from downstairs and Jo from upstairs. Never had Daddles had so many pats and pets. He jumped up on everyone, licked every hand and then came back to Peterkin and me to be hugged. There was a bit of chewed, ragged rope tied through his collar. We all thought the same thing — someone had taken Daddles and tried to keep him. Again he was awfully thin. Jo fed him and he split up that night, sleeping half of it with Peterkin and half with me. Peterkin said that was only fair. The next day we all went up to the Butlers to tell them the good news.

We got there kind of late, for we wanted to be sure Ben Butler was through work in his garden, so we landed about their suppertime — which comes early. It was awfully embarrassing for a moment. Then Betsy Eliza said if we'd stay and have supper with them she'd make pancakes. So Peterkin ran home cross-cut over the fields to tell Mother, and I stayed and laid the table. The Butlers made a lot of Daddles. They were certainly glad he was back safely.

Ben had made some good maple syrup in the spring so the pancakes were elegant. Daddles ate three, and two of Betsy Eliza's homemade sausages. After that he discovered the box back of the stove and for a few moments we were awfully worried.

The Butlers had a cat named Miranda — after Prospero's daughter in *The Tempest*. You see Betsy Eliza was a schoolteacher before she married Ben. She was terribly educated and knew Shakespeare better than we did. And we knew a lot. When Miranda had had kittens — four of them — they had named them Milly, Minnie, Mary and Martha. Their eyes were just open, and they were in the box back of the stove. Luckily for us Miranda was away; so when Daddles scrooched under the stove we didn't notice him until Betsy Eliza gave a funny little squeal and said, "Oh, look!"

Well — we looked; and there was Daddles with his head in the box, nuzzling the kittens. Of course the

Butlers didn't know how careful Daddles could be about partridge chicks and shuttlecocks. Peterkin said — almost sternly, "Don't get scared. Daddles wouldn't hurt anything new and soft." And, of course, he wouldn't. For a moment he talked to those kittens in his low whispering whimper. The next thing we knew he was walking around from the back of the stove with one of the kittens in his mouth. He brought it to me and dropped it in my lap, then sat up with his paw raised — just as if he was saying, "She's nice, isn't she?" She was, and not hurt, only a little damp.

It took only a few moments for him to bring over all the kittens; he dumped each one in our laps. They were all tiger-mixture; and one was what Ben called pure ink-milk-and-molasses. They were awfully cunning; and Daddles looked so proud as he watched us cuddle them you would have thought he had had the kittens himself. Peterkin and I were so pleased that we did not see Betsy Eliza growing more and more worried. And then it happened. Miranda appeared! The Butlers had cut a small hole in the woodshed and one in the pantry so that she could come and go as she pleased. And there she was — first looking in the box for the kittens and then stalking over to us with real tigerish eyes cast on Daddles. I guess she didn't like dogs.

Ben and Betsy Eliza tried to grab her. Peterkin tried to grab Daddles. For a moment we expected a regular cat-and-dog fight. Then Daddles settled it. He reached up for the kitten Peterkin had, took it carefully and just presented it to Miranda. He must have said something she understood, for she took the kitten and carried it back to the box. By the time she was back for another Daddles had it all ready for her, until all four kittens — Millie, Minnie, Martha and Mary — were safe in their box with their mother. Nobody said anything but Ben Butler. What he said was, "I swan! If I hadn't seen it with my own eyes I'd never had believed it." Betsy Eliza just wiped her eyes. As for Peterkin and me — we were just proud.

It was snug and warm and nice in the kitchen. The wood snapped in the stove, the kettle sang, and we talked. We talked about all the things we liked to remember about those two summers we had had Daddles: picking berries and buying his collar, having him warning us of the fire, helping catch Bill Monroe stealing the salmon — and winging him at it, my having scarlet fever. And I remembered again about our servant-candle and said it over to myself:

A candle is a small thing but it can kindle another.
You are such a light.
You can help to kindle the hearts of others.

I was thinking of Daddles. How much he had kindled other hearts since he had come to us. Leaving out, of course, the Monroe hearts. No one could kindle them.

There isn't much to tell about the end of that summer. But I haven't said anything about the doe and fawn that came back every summer in blueberry-time. The doe was always the same — we could tell by the tear in one ear; but the fawn was always a new one.

We had a small patch of blueberries below our house, near the shore. We kept it for emergencies — like when unexpected company came and Jo wanted to make a blueberry pie or some muffins in a hurry. Every summer — sometimes while Peterkin and I were picking — at least once in that summer — the doe would come with that fresh-new fawn of hers, its soft brown coat all speckled over with white. We would look up suddenly and there they would be. The doe never came very near, but the fawn always did; I guess she was curious, and I

84

guess the doe knew we would not harm her. Or him. Anyway, the fawn would nuzzle up to us, smell us, eat handfuls of blueberries until her mother said something like, "Come — that's enough!" And the two would go bounding off into the deep woods just beyond. Peterkin and I always thought they took us in on the way back from taking a salt lick on the shore. Some animals crave salt just like human beings.

The two summers Daddles was with us we thought he might mistake them for big rabbits or something and give chase. But he never did. Peterkin laid a quiet hand on him and he never even got to his feet. When the fawn nuzzled him he gave it a nice friendly lick.

That second summer the blackberries were especially thick. They grow best among the alder bushes. There they hang in clusters, big, juicy as black grapes — only better. The picking was hard. You had to push through the alder-tangle, and the briers would scratch arms and legs. Daddles hated blackberry-picking, but he always came along. He always found a spot where he could lie down and just wait patiently until our pails were full. We must have picked bushels. Jo made jam and jelly; Mother tried making blackberry brandy. But Peterkin and I liked them best in big bowls for lunch, along with glasses of milk and some of Jo's fresh-baked bread.

But the day came at last when Mother said if we brought back another pail of blackberries she would scream. So we picked for the neighbors who couldn't pick for themselves. We carried a pailful wherever we went to say good-by for the summer. Everywhere we got handouts — as always. Daddles liked that part. We

stopped at the Butlers, the Pendletons, Liza Bean's; and we even lugged a pailful down to Ellis Freeman. He was pleased. But every place we went somehow we grew sadder and sadder at leaving the Harbor. I don't know why.

When the stage drove down to take us to the boat Peterkin and I had big lumps in our throats. Daddles had spent the whole day with us, and he followed the stage as far as the Monroes. There he sat down, lifted a paw as if giving us a final salute, and watched the stage out of sight. I guess Ellis Freeman knew how sad we were to go; anyway he tried to cheer us up. "Look, Snoodie, I'll lay a wager with you and Peterkin. I'll wager another pail of them good blackberries ye'll be picking, come next summer, ag'inst another free ride to Belfast, that that hound-dog o' yourn will be waiting for you next June when you come back. He'll be up at the head of the lane — same as this year."

We agreed — kind of halfheartedly. But oh how we both hoped Ellis Freeman would win!

I REMEMBER it was a glowery day when the old *Katahdin* docked in Camden that next summer. Usually Peterkin and I enjoyed every minute of the trip down, but this time it was a doleful trip. To begin with, our father couldn't go down with us — that was a big disappointment. He was always fun. He also looked after Mother, who wasn't a good sailor. He called her "Grasshopper" — his pet name for her because she moved so quickly and was such a tiny person.

We always spent the night at the Parker House in Boston. That was fun. Then next day we shopped at S. S. Pierce and bought two barrels of stuff to have shipped down. Mother always let us pick out some of the things we especially liked such as Rose's Lime Juice.

After that we went to Webers and had chicken sandwiches and little cakes put up for our picnic supper on
the boat. The last thing we did was buy fruit at Faneuil
Hall Market. So we always landed on Rowe's Wharf
loaded.

Peterkin and I loved those old Boston and Bangor
boats. They were side-wheelers, resplendent with white
paint and gilt. Usually we were so happy to be going
to Maine that we skipped on board — at least I did,
and Peterkin jolly well was ready to turn handsprings.
But not this year. Early June had turned hot. I dragged
myself along after a tired mother and Jo. Peterkin
brought up the rear looking as glum and crotchety as a
horned owl.

Our staterooms were on the lee side of the boat — so
it was awfully uncomfortable and stuffy. As soon as
the old *Katahdin* was sailing down Boston Harbor we
brought our campstools out on the deck. Mother never
went down to the dining-saloon — as they called it
then. The food wasn't very good — and besides Mother
couldn't stand going below deck. So she ordered the
steward to bring pots of tea for herself and Jo and
milk for us.

I guess the milk must have been bad. It came straight from the cow in those days and didn't always keep well. Anyway, in the middle of the night Peterkin and I were awfully sick. We managed not to disturb Mother. As soon as we could we got to the rail outside. The only funny thing was that in the midst of disposing of everything Peterkin sang out to me, as he used to to Daddles, "Please turn your head the other way, Snoodie." That brought a giggle in spite of the way we felt.

As we began to feel better, Peterkin from the upper berth and I from the lower began to throw promises to each other of all the good times we would be having with Daddles. He was smack in the middle of everything we wished for. The boat always docked at Camden between six and seven in the morning. We all felt pretty droopy; but seeing Ellis Freeman at the foot of the gangplank to welcome us cheered us up considerably. I shouted down at him, "Hello, Mr. Freeman, have you seen Daddles?"

I guess he never heard me. He lifted Mother down gently to the dock, then grabbed the heaviest baggage and started jog-trotting down the wharf to where the teams were hitched. We gathered up most of what was left and followed him. When we got there — there was the Freemans' spanky-new two-seated buck-board and their best team of horses, the "prophets" — Elijah and Elisha. All the metal on the harness shone — even on that murky morning. Then Peterkin asked, "Which one of us won the wager, Mr. Freeman?"

Our stage driver was usually the kindest man in the world, but this time he snapped back at Peterkin, "Hain't you young-uns got eyes in your head? Doan't y' see I gotta make your mother comfortable and stow all this mess of luggage away so it won't slide any?" Then he acted kind of ashamed and added, "Where be them lumps of sugar you young-uns always fetch along to feed to 'Lisha and 'Lijah? Cal'ate they be expectin' 'em."

That was true. We always snitched sugar lumps from the Parker House to feed to the stage horses. So Peter-kin and I went round and fed them, patted them, and felt a bit better. I don't know why it is that children always want to find things as they have always been, like Father coming down with us each summer and the older brothers coming down for their vacations; and especially like having Daddles waiting for us at the head of the lane.

We climbed in the front seat with Ellis Freeman and kept quiet until we were off the wharf, out of the town, and had passed Sherman's Point. Then Mother broke the silence. "Isn't it about time you were telling us all the news at the Harbor?" I don't believe Mother felt as gay as she sounded, and I do believe Ellis tried his best to make everything sound as usual. He began sort of choking and speaking at the same time. "Seems like there hain't too much news this year. Old Man Thomas died come early spring — he of the moneybags." There he stopped.

By that time Peterkin and I couldn't hold in any longer. Peterkin asked, "Mr. Freeman, don't you think you should tell us who won the wager you made last fall?"

And I asked, "Is Daddles at the head of the lane?"

We had reached the Monroes' place then. The kitchen stoop was empty. Our stage driver reined the horses to a walk, cleared his throat, swallowed a couple of times; then it came. "I'm afeared he hain't, Snoodie. That plain hound-dog o' yourn got himself shot last fall — huntin'."

No one could say anything. I could hear Jo beginning to sniffle on the seat behind us. My throat had gone dry — as if I had swallowed sand. We got to our lane and oh how empty it looked! We shut our eyes, Peterkin and me, as we drove down to the cottage. Once there Peterkin spoke. "Who shot Daddles? Bill Monroe?" I guess for a moment there was murder in Peterkin's heart.

"Cal'ate it might have been — but no-wise intentional. Daddles was too good a rabbit-hound. Them Monroes jes' about live off rabbit and deer all winter. No — however it happened it must have been an accident, sure fur sartin."

We had reached the cottage at last. Ellis spoke to Mother. "Mrs. Wyman, ma'm, my son Stan is drivin' the regular stage today. The two of us kinda thought I might help a bit here with you folks." Then he was out of the buckboard. He lifted Mother down and began to lug in the luggage. Out of habit Peterkin and I lugged in our share. We always went in the kitchen way, but this time things were different. Inside, instead of the usual cold kitchen there was a fire in the stove. The two tables, the one Jo worked at and the one where she sat, were loaded with stuff.

For seconds we stood stockstill and just looked. There were chickens plucked and ready to cook, eggs, pies, sauces, biscuits, doughnuts, one of Betsy Eliza's cream-cakes and lots of glass jars with preserves, pickles, tomatoes and applesauce. Our stage driver gave it all one sweep of an arm. "Jes' Harbor folk. They kinda cal'-ated to give you a special welcome this year."

There were rocks in my stomach — I guess Peterkin had some, too. They anchored us to the floor until Mother spoke up real sharp. "You children get busy. Take up the bags. See that you put the right ones in each room. Change your clothes, and then come down and see what more you can do." She turned to Ellis Freeman. "We would be very much pleased if you would stay and have breakfast with us. It would make it easier for all of us, I think."

Ellis Freeman stayed. When we came down he was washing up at the sink. Mother had put the bright red-and-white checked cloth on the table by the windows. She told us to lay places for our stage driver and Jo. Jo was frying bacon and making a huge omelet in the big spider. The coffee smelled good. But Peterkin and I couldn't eat anything. We couldn't take any milk, remembering the night before. So Mother made us cambric coffee and we found that tasted good.

After breakfast Ellis Freeman did a mighty kind thing. He invited us all to have a drive in the buckboard — anywhere we wanted to go. Mother looked at us and we shook our heads; so she thanked him and said she thought we had better keep busy for the rest of the day, putting things to rights in the cottage.

She certainly did keep us busy. Peterkin and I laid fires in all the downstairs fireplaces, and in the potbellied stove in Mother's room. Then we filled all the wood-baskets. Peterkin chopped kindling and I brought it in. After that we lugged all the empty valises and telescope-bags up to the attic. The last thing we had to do was to make up the beds. That was a chore. Blankets to take out of mothballs, clean sheets and comforters to take out of the chests. Afterwards we knew how wise Mother had been to keep us working hard.

Before we finished good smells were coming from the kitchen. Jo was pan-roasting the chickens. I asked Peterkin, "Think you can eat any supper?" "Maybe," said he. And that's all the talking we did all day.

It was dusk when we went down to the kitchen to

ask Jo what she was fixing to go with the chicken. But before she could answer we heard a big thud of feet on the stoop, the door opened and Ben Butler came stamping in. "Hi there, Peterkin, hi, Snoodie!" he called out as he had always done. Then, taking a good look at us, he went over to Jo. "Hi, there, Irishwoman! Do ye cal'ate by any chance there might be enough supper for me to sit down for a bite with you-uns? Betsy Eliza scrimped me aplenty on my supper — had it early, likewise."

Jo said that seeing as how they were probably his chickens in the first place she "cal'ated" he might have the back of one of them. They both tried to laugh at that, but it wasn't very hearty. Then Mother came in and made him extra welcome. We were glad he stayed. The chicken tasted awfully good; and when it came time to cut Betsy Eliza's cream-cake we cut ourselves terribly big slices. Ben noticed and nodded his approval. "See you young-uns hain't lost your appetite for one of Betsy Eliza's best. When I tell her she'll be mighty pleased."

Everyone had finished supper and pushed back his chair when Mother spoke: "Ben — if you have anything more you can tell the children about Daddles I wish you would. They know so little. It would help them, I think."

So Ben told — told the whole miserable story. After we left in the fall he noticed every two or three days Daddles would lope past on the road to our lane. And there he would wait for us — same as always. "Seems like that hound-dog jes' couldn't get it through his head that you, Peterkin — and you, Snoodie — had gone for the winter. Then November come with a light fall of snow. For the next three days there was no sign of Daddles, no paw-prints on the snow along the road. That night after supper I told Betsy Eliza I was goin' down to them Monroes and see was Daddles all right."

In the end Bill Monroe had owned up — he had shot Daddles. Didn't mean to — just a miserable accident. He and Mat were waiting in the beech-wood for the rabbit to double back; but instead of one rabbit there were two — and Daddles was close on them. Bill Monroe got rattled and shot carelessly. He got one rabbit and Daddles. That was how it happened. Ben Butler went on, "Got him to tell me where in the beech-wood he'd left him and come the next mornin' I took a spade, a bit of old quilt Betsy Eliza gave me, and some black paint. Found Daddles just where Bill said he was — in that patch of woods where you young-uns go every June to git your mother her ladyslipper. Purtiest place there is."

So Ben had made a grave for Daddles, wrapped the quilt around him, covered him snug. Afterwards he pushed up the big slab-faced rock to mark one end and planted a small spruce tree at the other. On the slab-side of the rock he printed DADDLES — plain for all to read; and underneath the dates of the two years he had belonged to us. "Cal'ated all the rest of the time didn't matter to that hound-dog."

Peterkin asked just one question: "Was he wearing his collar?"

"Sure was. Buried it on him. Kinda reasoned you two would like it that away."

We nodded.

Mother sent us to bed early. I asked could I carry in the servant-candle and have it in my room. Of course Mother said, "Yes." I don't know how much Peterkin slept. I didn't much, kept waking up. But it was a comfort to see that red eye looking at me — as if it was saying, "It's going to be all right, Snoodie." But every time I waked up I found I was reaching down under the comforter to feel Daddles — just as I had through the long sick nights when I'd had scarlet fever.

Next morning, when we'd done our chores, we went up to the beech-woods. We found where Daddles was without searching. It was just where Ben Butler said, the prettiest spot on the whole mountainside, and where we had sat so often while Daddles was running a rabbit around Bald Peak. Ladyslippers — lots of them — were in bloom there — not that Daddles would have cared a hoot. Ben Butler had fixed it nice. The little spruce was a sturdy tree. We liked it. Peterkin and I sat down on the log — we just sat. I spoke the only thing we said for a long time: "Peterkin, do you think God has made a small dog-heaven for nice dogs like Daddles?"

"Could be," said Peterkin.

We sat some more. I thought a short, silly little prayer, but it comforted me: "Dear God. If you have a dog-heaven please make Daddles welcome there. We would like to find him safe in your care when we come aloft. Thank you. Amen."

After clearing the woods we ran all the way home.

I thought some more as I ran. Given time we would be remembering Daddles with just happy remembrances — we would be able to talk about him without feeling rocks in our stomachs. And if one had a sorrow, Maine was the best place to be.